The Story of Sparky® the Fire Dog

NATIONAL FIRE PROTECTION ASSOCIATION
The leading information and knowledge resource on fire, electrical and related hazards

Printed in the United States of America

ISBN (book): 978-1-4559-2113-3

Printed in the United States of America

22 23 24 25 26 9 8 7 6 5

For more fire-safety information: www.nfpa.org/education

For fire-safety fun for the whole family: www.sparky.org

A few years ago,
a Dalmatian puppy sat
outside the fence at the school.
The puppy loved watching the
children play games and laugh.

He wanted to go inside and play with the children. But, he was very shy.

He spent his days running back
and forth along the fence,
sometimes barking "hello."

One day, the puppy followed two children home from school. He watched them go inside their house. Then he curled up under a tree to take a nap.

The puppy woke up. He could smell smoke! He saw smoke and flames. The children's house was on fire.

The puppy knew he needed to get help right away. He ran down the street to the fire station, barking all the way.

The puppy saw the firefighters
jump into the fire truck and leave.

He tried to run behind them, but his little legs could not keep up.

He ran back to the house. The street was filled with fire trucks, hoses, and lots of people. The puppy could not find the kids. He was worried.

13

The firefighters worked very hard
to put out the fire. They got back
into the fire truck. Then Firefighter
Janet noticed the sad puppy.

"Look it's the little puppy we saw barking at the station," she said.

Firefighter Janet picked up the puppy. Her arms felt safe. The puppy could not stop thinking about the kids.

"Let's take him to
the neighbor's house," said the
firefighter. "The kids are there.
Maybe he can cheer them up."

Firefighter Janet carried the puppy to the neighbor's house.

The puppy could not
believe his eyes!

The children were safe!
The puppy jumped out of
Firefighter Janet's arms.

His tail wagged faster than ever
before. The children hugged the
puppy. They felt a little bit better.

"Do you know who this puppy belongs to?" Firefighter Janet asked. The children did not know. But they had seen him at school.

24

"Well, he's a real hero," said Firefighter Janet. "He ran all the way to the fire station to let us know there was a fire at your house."

"I guess that makes him a fire dog," said Firefighter Janet. "We should call him Sparky. That's it — Sparky the Fire Dog."

"Sparky can live with us at the fire station," she said, "but you kids can visit him any time you want."

Sparky was very proud of his new
name. He loved his new home
at the fire station.

He worked hard to teach
children and their families
all about fire safety.

Can you help Sparky find his outside meeting place?

Follow the path to Sparky's outside meeting place, the tree in his front yard, by going from A-Z in alphabetical order.

Outside Meeting Place

START HERE!